JANUARY
·2011·

DECEMBER 2010

S	M	T	W	T	F	S
			1	2	3	4
5	6	7	8	9	10	11
12	13	14	15	16	17	18
19	20	21	22	23	24	25
26	27	28	29	30	31	

FEBRUARY

S	M	T	W	T	F	S
		1	2	3	4	5
6	7	8	9	10	11	12
13	14	15	16	17	18	19
20	21	22	23	24	25	26
27	28					

Sunday	Monday	Tuesday	Wednesday	Thursday	Friday	Saturday
						1 New Year's Day
2	3	4 ●	5	6	7	8
9	10 Coming of Age Day (Japan)	11	12 ◐	13	14	15
16	17 Martin Luther King, Jr. Day	18	19 ○	20	21	22
23 / 30	24 / 31	25	26 ◑ Australia Day (Australia)	27	28	29

Love true.
Family.
FRIENDS.
Life.
CHOCOLATE.
Karen Good

FEBRUARY
·2011·

Sunday	Monday	Tuesday	Wednesday	Thursday	Friday	Saturday
		1	2 Groundhog Day	● 3 Chinese New Year	4	5
6 Waitangi Day (New Zealand)	7	8	9	10	◐ 11 National Foundation Day (Japan)	12 Abraham Lincoln's Birthday
13	14 Valentine's Day	15 Flag Day (Canada)	16	17	○ 18	19
20	21 Presidents' Day	22 George Washington's Birthday	23	◑ 24	25	26
27	28					

JANUARY

S	M	T	W	T	F	S
						1
2	3	4	5	6	7	8
9	10	11	12	13	14	15
16	17	18	19	20	21	22
23	24	25	26	27	28	29
30	31					

MARCH

S	M	T	W	T	F	S
		1	2	3	4	5
6	7	8	9	10	11	12
13	14	15	16	17	18	19
20	21	22	23	24	25	26
27	28	29	30	31		

good day, sunshine.
Dorothy was right . . .
There's no place like home.
Just click your heels
three times.
Karen Good

MARCH
·2011·

Sunday	Monday	Tuesday	Wednesday	Thursday	Friday	Saturday
FEBRUARY S M T W T F S 1 2 3 4 5 6 7 8 9 10 11 12 13 14 15 16 17 18 19 20 21 22 23 24 25 26 27 28		1	2	3	● 4	5
6	7	8 Mardi Gras Day	9 Ash Wednesday	10	11	◐ 12
13 Daylight Saving Time Begins	14 Canberra Day (Australia)	15	16	17 St. Patrick's Day	18	○ 19 Purim Begins at Sundown
20 First Day of Spring	21	22	23	24	25	◑ 26
27	28	29	30	31		APRIL S M T W T F S 1 2 3 4 5 6 7 8 9 10 11 12 13 14 15 16 17 18 19 20 21 22 23 24 25 26 27 28 29 30

Happy Springtime
CELEBRATE
ALL THE GOOD STUFF.
Karen Good

APRIL
·2011·

Sunday	Monday	Tuesday	Wednesday	Thursday	Friday	Saturday
	MARCH S M T W T F S 1 2 3 4 5 6 7 8 9 10 11 12 13 14 15 16 17 18 19 20 21 22 23 24 25 26 27 28 29 30 31		MAY S M T W T F S 1 2 3 4 5 6 7 8 9 10 11 12 13 14 15 16 17 18 19 20 21 22 23 24 25 26 27 28 29 30 31		1 April Fool's Day	2
3 Mothering Sunday (UK)	4	5	6	7	8	9
10	11	12	13	14	15	16
17 Palm Sunday	18 Passover Begins at Sundown	19	20	21	22 Good Friday Earth Day	23
24 Easter Sunday	25 Easter Monday (Australia, Canada, New Zealand, UK) Anzac Day (Australia, New Zealand)	26	27 Administrative Professionals Day	28	29 Arbor Day Showa Day (Japan)	30

Plant so many posies.
Violets
Zinnias
Petunias
JUST BELIEVE.
KEEP THE FAITH.
Pretty flowers are very good for you.

MAY
·2011·

Sunday	Monday	Tuesday	Wednesday	Thursday	Friday	Saturday
1 May Day	2 Bank Holiday (UK)	3 National Teacher Day / Constitution Day (Japan)	4 Greenery Day (Japan)	5 Cinco de Mayo / Children's Day (Japan)	6	7
8 Mother's Day	9	10	11	12	13	14
15	16	17	18	19	20	21 Armed Forces Day
22	23 Victoria Day (Canada)	24	25	26	27	28
29	30 Memorial Day Observance / Spring Bank Holiday (UK)	31				

APRIL

S	M	T	W	T	F	S
					1	2
3	4	5	6	7	8	9
10	11	12	13	14	15	16
17	18	19	20	21	22	23
24	25	26	27	28	29	30

JUNE

S	M	T	W	T	F	S
			1	2	3	4
5	6	7	8	9	10	11
12	13	14	15	16	17	18
19	20	21	22	23	24	25
26	27	28	29	30		

Chase Butterflies
Run
with
the wind
Go be
free.
Feel the cool grass beneath your feet.
Karen Good

JUNE
·2011·

Sunday	Monday	Tuesday	Wednesday	Thursday	Friday	Saturday
MAY S M T W T F S 1 2 3 4 5 6 7 8 9 10 11 12 13 14 15 16 17 18 19 20 21 22 23 24 25 26 27 28 29 30 31		JULY S M T W T F S 1 2 3 4 5 6 7 8 9 10 11 12 13 14 15 16 17 18 19 20 21 22 23 24 25 26 27 28 29 30 31	● 1	2	3	4
5 Canadian Forces Day (Canada)	6	7	8	◐ 9	10	11
12	13	14 Flag Day	○ 15	16	17	18
19 Father's Day	20	21 First Day of Summer	22	◑ 23	24 St-Jean Baptiste Day (Quebec)	25
26	27	28	29	30		

It's a blue skies day.
Linger awhile in your daydreams.
Karen Good

JULY
·2011·

Sunday	Monday	Tuesday	Wednesday	Thursday	Friday	Saturday
	(June mini-calendar)		(August mini-calendar)		● 1 Canada Day (Canada)	2
3	4 Independence Day	5	6	7	◐ 8	9
10	11	12	13	14	○ 15	16
17	18 Ocean Day (Japan)	19	20	21	22	◑ 23
24 / 31 Ramadan Begins at Sundown (NA)	25	26	27	28	29	● 30

JUNE

S	M	T	W	T	F	S
			1	2	3	4
5	6	7	8	9	10	11
12	13	14	15	16	17	18
19	20	21	22	23	24	25
26	27	28	29	30		

AUGUST

S	M	T	W	T	F	S
	1	2	3	4	5	6
7	8	9	10	11	12	13
14	15	16	17	18	19	20
21	22	23	24	25	26	27
28	29	30	31			

SOMETIMES
THE TINIEST
MATTERS
Just Because
FEEL
GREAT
BIG!
Karen Good

AUGUST
·2011·

Sunday	Monday	Tuesday	Wednesday	Thursday	Friday	Saturday
	1 Civic Holiday (Canada)	2	3	4	5	◐ 6
7	8	9	10	11	12	○ 13
14	15	16	17	18	19	20
◑ 21	22	23	24	25	26	27
28	● 29 Summer Bank Holiday (UK)	30	31			

JULY

S	M	T	W	T	F	S
					1	2
3	4	5	6	7	8	9
10	11	12	13	14	15	16
17	18	19	20	21	22	23
24	25	26	27	28	29	30
31						

SEPTEMBER

S	M	T	W	T	F	S
				1	2	3
4	5	6	7	8	9	10
11	12	13	14	15	16	17
18	19	20	21	22	23	24
25	26	27	28	29	30	

Take joy in simple pleasures.
See all the beautiful things.

SEPTEMBER

·2011·

Sunday	Monday	Tuesday	Wednesday	Thursday	Friday	Saturday
AUGUST S M T W T F S 1 2 3 4 5 6 7 8 9 10 11 12 13 14 15 16 17 18 19 20 21 22 23 24 25 26 27 28 29 30 31		OCTOBER S M T W T F S 1 2 3 4 5 6 7 8 9 10 11 12 13 14 15 16 17 18 19 20 21 22 23 24 25 26 27 28 29 30 31		1	2	3
◐ 4 Father's Day (New Zealand)	5 Labor Day / Labour Day (Canada)	6	7	8	9	10
11 Patriot Day / Grandparents' Day	○ 12	13	14	15	16	17
18	19 Respect for the Aged Day (Japan)	◑ 20	21 International Day of Peace	22	23 First Day of Autumn	24
25	26 Family Day	● 27	28 Rosh Hashanah Begins at Sundown	29	30	

Sometimes
you just
have to laugh.
Karen Good

OCTOBER
·2011·

Sunday	Monday	Tuesday	Wednesday	Thursday	Friday	Saturday
	SEPTEMBER S M T W T F S 1 2 3 4 5 6 7 8 9 10 11 12 13 14 15 16 17 18 19 20 21 22 23 24 25 26 27 28 29 30		NOVEMBER S M T W T F S 1 2 3 4 5 6 7 8 9 10 11 12 13 14 15 16 17 18 19 20 21 22 23 24 25 26 27 28 29 30			1
2	3	4 ◐	5	6	7 Yom Kippur Begins at Sundown	8
9 National Children's Day	10 Columbus Day Observance; Thanksgiving Day (Canada); Health and Sports Day (Japan)	11	12 ○	13	14	15 Sweetest Day
16 National Boss Day	17	18	19	20 ◑	21	22
23 / 30	24 Labour Day (New Zealand); Breast Cancer Awareness Day / 31 Halloween	25	26 ●	27	28	29

Ever so grateful.
I don't need much,
I just need enough.
Karen GOOD

NOVEMBER
·2011·

Sunday	Monday	Tuesday	Wednesday	Thursday	Friday	Saturday
		1 All Saints Day	2	3 Culture Day (Japan)	4	5
6 Daylight Saving Time Ends	7	8 Election Day	9	10	11 Veterans Day / Remembrance Day (Canada, UK)	12
13	14	15	16	17	18	19
20	21	22	23 Labor Thanksgiving Day (Japan)	24 Thanksgiving Day	25	26
27	28	29	30			

OCTOBER

S	M	T	W	T	F	S
						1
2	3	4	5	6	7	8
9	10	11	12	13	14	15
16	17	18	19	20	21	22
23	24	25	26	27	28	29
30	31					

DECEMBER

S	M	T	W	T	F	S
				1	2	3
4	5	6	7	8	9	10
11	12	13	14	15	16	17
18	19	20	21	22	23	24
25	26	27	28	29	30	31

Joy to the World.
. . . AND VIRGINIA,
THE ANSWER
IS YES.
KarenGOOD

DECEMBER

·2011·

Sunday	Monday	Tuesday	Wednesday	Thursday	Friday	Saturday
NOVEMBER S M T W T F S 1 2 3 4 5 6 7 8 9 10 11 12 13 14 15 16 17 18 19 20 21 22 23 24 25 26 27 28 29 30		JANUARY 2012 S M T W T F S 1 2 3 4 5 6 7 8 9 10 11 12 13 14 15 16 17 18 19 20 21 22 23 24 25 26 27 28 29 30 31		1	◐ 2	3
4	5	6	7 Pearl Harbor Remembrance Day	8	9	○ 10
11	12	13	14	15	16	17
◑ 18	19	20 Hanukkah Begins at Sundown	21	22 First Day of Winter	23 The Emperor's Birthday (Japan)	● 24
25 Christmas Day	Kwanzaa Begins 26 Boxing Day (Australia, Canada, New Zealand, UK)	27 Christmas Observance (Australia, New Zealand, UK)	28	29	30	31 New Year's Eve

Hello friends,
Welcome to the New Year.
May yours be filled with
plenty of good laughs,
nice people and
lot's of pretty posies.
Thank You
for supporting my work.
Happy Dreams,
Karen H. Good